TIME TO SHARE Jornadas

Workbook 9

Organizadora:
Editora Saraiva
Obra coletiva organizada e produzida pela Editora Saraiva

Editor responsável:
Vicente Martínez
Licenciado em Tradução/Interpretação pela Universidad Pontificia de Comillas (Madrid)
Editor de conteúdos didáticos

Coordenadora:
Gisele Aga
Licenciada em Letras pela FMU – Faculdades Metropolitanas Unidas
Professora de Inglês na rede particular de ensino e em cursos de idiomas
Coordenadora pedagógica em cursos de idiomas
Editora de conteúdos didáticos

Editora Saraiva

PRESENTATION

Caro estudante,

Este caderno foi elaborado com a finalidade de ajudá-lo a organizar seu conhecimento. Ao resolver as atividades propostas, você terá a oportunidade de buscar informações, utilizar a própria experiência e conhecimento prévio sobre os assuntos tratados, desenvolver habilidades, elaborar opiniões sobre assuntos da atualidade, refletir sobre atitudes e comportamentos e ampliar a sua visão do mundo.

As atividades estão distribuídas em oito unidades, correspondendo às unidades do livro para que possa retomar e ampliar os tópicos estudados. A cada unidade, você encontrará as seguintes seções: *Review the journey*, *Another look* e *Reading the world*.

- Em *Review the journey*, você irá aplicar os conceitos gramaticais apresentados na unidade.
- A seção *Another look* propõe uma leitura complementar (verbal ou não verbal) ligada a algum tema ou gênero trabalhado na unidade do livro. As atividades visam trabalhar aspectos que não foram abordados no livro ou que são tratados sob outro aspecto. Além disso, nas últimas atividades você será incentivado a refletir e se posicionar em relação ao assunto tratado na seção.
- Em *Reading the world*, você lerá textos com temáticas instigantes, como aspectos culturais de diversos países, novas tecnologias, entre outras. Ao final das atividades, você poderá contar com uma produção (oral ou escrita).

Esperamos que sua jornada por este caderno seja bastante produtiva e o auxilie a desenvolver a autonomia nos estudos.

Os editores

CONTENTS

UNIT 1

Be positive!

Review the journey

1. Read the text. Check the sentences with the present perfect tense.

www.huffingtonpost.com/karl-a-pillemer-phd/listening-to-elders_b_4200329.html

7 QUESTIONS WE NEED TO ASK EVERY OLDER PERSON

PHOTOS 12 CINEMA/UNIVERSALPICTURES/DIOMEDIA

An ageless friendship between Ninny and Evelyn (*Fried Green Tomatoes*, directed by Jon Avnet).

- [ ] What are some of the most important lessons you feel you have learned over the course of your life?
- [ ] Some people say that they have had difficult or stressful experiences but they have learned important lessons from them. Is that true for you? Can you give examples of what you learned?
- [ ] As you look back over your life, do you see any "turning points"; that is, a key event or experience that changed over the course of your life or set you on a different track?
- [ ] What's the secret to a happy marriage?
- [ ] What are some of the important choices or decisions you made that you have learned from?
- [ ] What would you say you know now about living a happy and successful life that you didn't know when you were twenty?
- [ ] What would you say are the major values or principles that you live by?

Extracted from: <www.huffingtonpost.com/karl-a-pillemer-phd/listening-to-elders_b_4200329.html>. Accessed on: Apr. 12, 2016.

2. Ask an elderly person questions about their life experiences. Use the words given in parentheses and add any other necessary words. Write the answers, too.

a. ______________________________? (ever / plant)

____

b. ______________________________? (ever / travel)

____

3. Use the verbs from the box in the present perfect to complete the quotes.

be	not change	take	waste

INTI ST CLAIR/BLEND IMAGES RM/GETTY IMAGES

a. The great secret that all old people share is that you really ______________ in seventy or eighty years. Your body changes, but you don't change at all. And that, of course, causes great confusion.

Doris Lessing

Extracted from: <www.huffingtonpost.com/karl-a-pillemer-phd/listening-to-elders_b_4200329.html>. Accessed on: Apr. 12, 2016.

b. If I had known I was going to live this long, I would ______________ better care of myself.

Mae West

Extracted from: <www.goodreads.com/quotes/tag/old-age>. Accessed on: Apr. 12, 2016.

c. A man who views the world the same at fifty as he did at twenty, ______________ thirty years of his life.

Muhammad Ali

Extracted from: <www.spiritual-quotes-to-live-by.com/aging-quotes.html>. Accessed on: Apr. 12, 2016.

d. Wrinkles should merely indicate where the smiles ______________.

Mark Twain

Adapted from: <https://jasreflections.files.wordpress.com/2011/03/mark-twain.jpg>. Accessed on: Apr. 12, 2016.

4. Ask a friend and check his/her answers.

If he/she	Yes	No
a. has lived in the countryside.		
b. has published anything on the internet recently.		
c. has played a computer game this week.		
d. has already moved to another city.		
e. has already been to a concert.		

Another look

1. Take a look at the text below. Where could you find it? Circle the correct answer.

a. In a comic book. **b.** In the web. **c.** In an encyclopedia.

2. Which features can you identify in the text? Check the correct answer(s).

a. ☐ title and subheadings
b. ☐ informal style
c. ☐ timelines
d. ☐ quotes

3. According to the text features, we can say it is

a. ☐ a fictional story.
b. ☐ a biography.
c. ☐ a diary entry.
d. ☐ an article.

4. Observe the picture and read the title. Then circle the best option to complete the sentence.

The text is about **younger/older** people and **physical/mental** exercises.

5. Read the title of the text. What do you expect to read? Write a short paragraph with your ideas. Then, read the text and check if your ideas are correct.

____

____

____

6. Read the text again. Then, correct the sentences according to what you read.

BIS

www.medicalnewstoday.com/articles/308289.php

Exercise in older age may protect memory and thinking skills

Written by Honor Whiteman
Published: Thursday, March 24, 2016

Moderate to high-intensity exercise in older age may slow cognitive decline, say researchers.

INDIA PICTURE/SHUTTERSTOCK

Dr. Clinton B. Wright, of the University of Miami in Florida, and colleagues found that adults over the age of 50 who engaged in light or no exercise experienced a significantly faster decline in memory and thinking skills, compared with those who engaged in moderate to intense exercise.

And another study reported last October found that regular aerobic exercise during middle and older age may help keep the brain healthy, protecting against behavioral deficits and age-related inflammation in areas of the brain linked to memory and thinking.

It seems studies like these are in abundance, but researchers note that it is important to understand how lifestyle factors may help slow cognitive decline, especially with an aging population.

"The number of people over the age of 65 in the United States is on the rise, meaning the public health burden of thinking and memory problems will likely grow," notes Dr. Wright.

"Our study showed that for older people, getting regular exercise may be protective, helping them keep their cognitive abilities longer."

Adapted from: <www.medicalnewstoday.com/articles/308289.php>. Accessed on: Apr. 12, 2016.

a. Light or no exercise may slow cognitive decline in adults over 50 years old.
Moderate to intense exercise may slow cognitive decline in adults over 50 years old.

b. If you are middle-aged, aerobic exercise may keep your heart healthy.

____

c. Slow cognitive decline is common among youngsters.

____

d. There are fewer people over sixty-five in the US now than ten years ago.

____

7. Research about Brazil and answer: Is Brazilian population living longer too? What is the life expectancy average in your state?

____

____

____

____

____

8. According to your findings about Brazil, can the research you read about help aging Brazilians live longer and better? Why?

____

____

____

1. Why is it important to have studies about different stages of our lives?

____

____

____

2. How elder-friendly is your neighborhood? Are there any parks, gyms or fitness centers to help older adults exercise?

____

____

____

Reading the world

1. Is there a Respect for the Aged Day or a Grandparent's Day in Brazil? When is it? How do you celebrate it?

2. Are there laws that protect the elderly in Brazil? What do you know about them?

3. Read the text and do the following activities.

What is Respect for the Aged Day?

1 The third Monday of September is Respect for the Aged Day, a national holiday in Japan. The Japanese call national holidays "red days" because they appear in red print on the calendar. As this will make September 12–14 a long weekend, be prepared for heavier than usual traffic and crowded trains if you are traveling.

2 Japanese people traditionally wear red on their 60th birthday because 60 years is one cycle on the Chinese calendar and after 60, it is said that you become a baby again. Babies in Japan are called "aka-chan" or "red one."

3 Respect for the Aged Day, called *keiro no hi*, is not quite like "Grandparent's Day" in the U.S. It is far more serious. Neighborhoods will have volunteers distribute free "obento" boxed lunches to elderly people in the neighborhood and smaller villages will hold *keirokai* shows where the younger people and school children prepare dances and songs for a special *keirokai* ceremony. The elderly attendees are also treated to lunch, tea, and sweets after the performance.

W DEON/SHUTTERSTOCK

4 As Japan's nation grays and people get older and older, some of these traditions may change, however. On the small island of 700 people where I live, the *keirokai* ceremony used to be held for those 60 years old and over. But with so many people over the age of 60 now, the qualifying age to attend the *keirokai* has steadily increased, and is now 65. As Japan's society ages and nursing homes become more popular, being old may not be so special anymore—but rather the norm.

5 Respect for the Aged Day is also a way to honor longevity, and Japanese people have always been some of the longest living in the world. But this is also changing as more and more Japanese people add meat and other western foods to their diets. In addition, city living is seen to cut lifespan due to pollution and stress.

Extracted from: <www.planettokyo.com/blog/japanese-culture/what-is-respect-for-the-aged-day/>. Accessed on: Apr. 13, 2016.

4. Read the text again and write the number of the paragraph in which we find the answers for the following questions.

a. What does the expression *red days* refer to? ______

b. What is the name of the special ceremony that happens in some villages? ______

c. What is the meaning of *keiro no hi* in English? ______

d. Which expression is equivalent to *also* or *additionally*? ______

5. Now answer the questions from activity 4.

a. ______

b. ______

c. ______

d. ______

6. Circle the words associated to **age** and **aging**.

aged birthday ceremony crowded elderly longevity older popular

7. Think about how Brazilians treat their elders in general. Consider these images and write true sentences about your reality.

a.

FERNANDO FAVORETTO/CRIAR IMAGEM

______

______

b.

BOJAN MILINKOV/SHUTTERSTOCK

______

______

8. What would you propose to improve the quality of life for the elderly in your city or neighborhood? Write down your proposals and explain how you would implement them.

______

______

______

______

UNIT 2

Will you write to an advice column?

Review the journey

1. Read the text. Underline the correct pronouns to complete the paragraph.

www.askdrm.org/col_teens.html

ASKDRM

– November 23, 2015 –

Hi! I am a high school student in Korea. I have a problem, so I want to get some advice from you. I am worried about sleeping too much in school. Since entering high school last year, I have been so tired every day that I sleep in all classes of the day, even during evening self-study time. Regardless of whether the class is boring or interesting, I fall asleep and I don't even know when I fall asleep in class. But teachers who don't know about my problem often misunderstand me because I sleep so much in their class. For example, last year, my math teacher became very angry at me. Thinking that my sleeping reflected a bad class attitude, she reduced my score to almost the lowest for my attitude in class, thinking I was ignoring her. And last winter, I couldn't go to China to experience its culture through a school program because some teachers kept me from joining the school program because they think I have a bad attitude in class. I try hard to break my habit of sleeping in class. I sleep at midnight, and wake up at 6:30 am every day. And I sit in front of the classroom to avoid sleeping in class. But I still sleep in class EVERY DAY! My friends have counseled me about my worry several times, but I only get the same answers every time like 'go to sleep early', 'sit in the front row', etc. I know if I sleep in class, I won't achieve my dream and improve my grades. But I can't seem to avoid falling asleep. I wait for your sincere advice. Please help me!

– Sylvia, 17

Dear Sylvia,

Although you may be trying to get more sleep, six and half hours may not be sufficient for you. Most teens need at least eight or nine hours to feel rested. A student might fall asleep in class once in a while because the material is boring or the classroom is warm or she/he hasn't slept enough the night before. But there also might be a physical or psychological reason for your constant sleepiness. Make an appointment with a doctor as soon as possible to check out the various possibilities. What you do next really depends on what, if anything, a doctor finds. And if the problem is simply that you're not getting enough sleep, arrange your schedule so that you go to sleep earlier than you do now and make sure you're not doing anything (like drinking coffee or watching a scary movie) that will prevent you from getting to sleep at a reasonable hour.

– Dr M

Extracted from: <www.askdrm.org/col_teens.html>. Accessed on: Apr. 13, 2016.

Sylvia is a 17-year-old student who is worried about **she/hers/herself**. Dr. M. is a column advisor. Sylvia has written **her/she** a question asking for advice. Some of **her/she/herself** teachers get angry because she can't help sleeping in class. Do **you/yourself/your** sometimes struggle to stay awake in class?

2. Use reflexive pronouns to complete the sentences.

a. Sylvia should try to help ________________ by resting longer.

b. Sylvia's friends have probably advised her to sit in the front row by ________________.

c. Some teens cannot solve their problems ________________.

d. I ________________ shouldn't go to bed so late every single night.

3. Match both columns.

a. If Sylvia sleeps less than she should,	☐	she will most probably fail school.
b. Dr. M. believes that if Sylvia sees a doctor,	☐	he/she'd better do something about it.
c. If Sylvia doesn't get any help,	☐	you won't do well in your tests.
d. If you drink too much coffee,	☐	he/she will be able to help her.
e. If someone often feels very tired,	☐	you can have a stomachache.
f. I think that if you don't pay attention in class,	☐	she falls asleep in class.

4. Finish the sentences with information about yourself.

a. When I want to have fun, I usually ________________.

b. When something stresses me, ________________.

c. When I'm by myself, ________________.

d. If I can't make a decision by myself, ________________.

5. Use the appropriate form of the verbs in parentheses.

Someday in the future I ________________ (travel) to many different countries if I have a chance to. If I ________________ (study) many foreign languages, I ________________ (be able to) talk to more and more people around the world. If that ________________ (happen), I ________________ (collect) different testimonials about living in other countries. Then, if I ________________ (have) the chance, I ________________ (make) a movie about my experiences.

RUBBERBALL/DIOMEDIA

Another look

1. Take a look at the text below and choose the alternative that completes each sentence correctly.

a. The material intends to

☐ promote a photo exhibition. ☐ instruct people about a subject.

b. There are

☐ questions, answers, comments and other visual elements.

☐ pictures and a game.

c. The text is a

☐ news article. ☐ blog post. ☐ poster.

2. Read the text and answer: Where could we find this material?

____

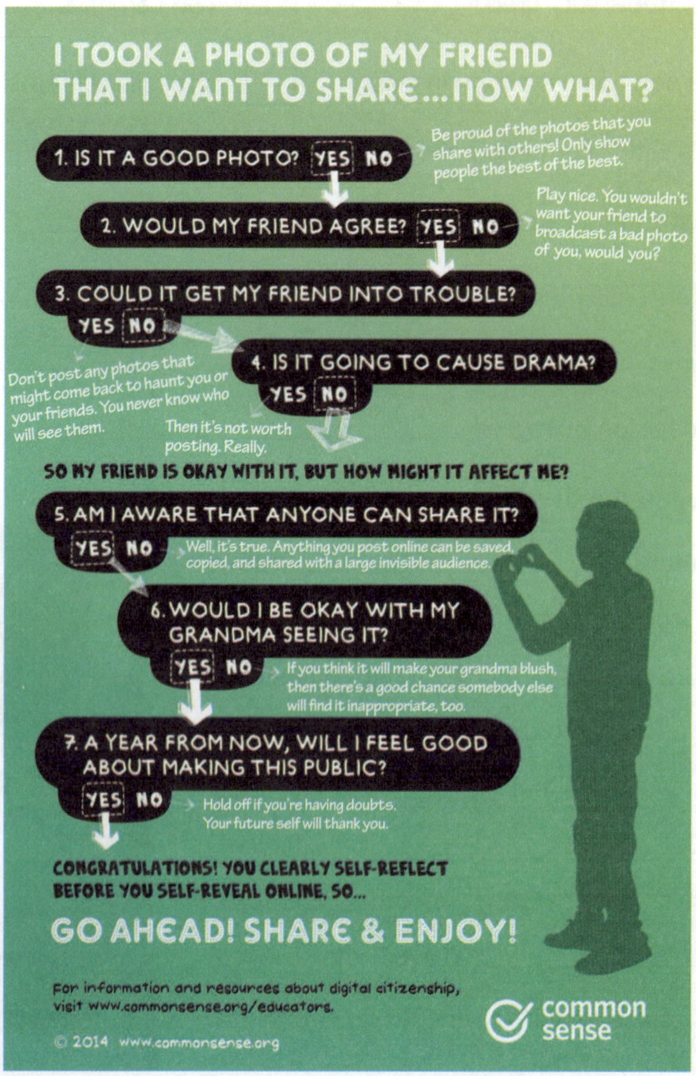

©COMMON SENSE EDUCATION/WWW.COMMONSENSEMEDIA.ORG

3. Read the text again and answer.

a. If you take a picture with friends, but they don't like it, should you post it? Explain.

____

____

b. Is it possible to know how many people (and who) will see the photos you post?

____

____

c. What does it mean to think about your grandmother's opinion?

____

____

4. Write **T** (true) or **F** (false).

a. ☐ You will hurt your friend if he/she doesn't approve your post.

b. ☐ Some of the things we post online shouldn't be shared.

c. ☐ Think twice before sharing any personal content.

d. ☐ If you are in doubt about sharing something, reflect about it first and then talk to the people that are part of the photo to make a decision.

5. What advice would you give someone who has posted something inappropriate? How would you tell him/her?

____

____

____

____

1. Have you or anybody you know ever posted anything you or he/she regretted?

____

____

2. Do you know how to report cyberbullying in your school/community/country?

____

____

Reading the world

1. Read the text and say whether you would write to an advice column asking for help if you were this person. Justify your answer.

____

____

A Positive Image

Written By: Amrita Dixit, teen writer

CRSHELARE/SHUTTERSTOCK

Sometimes when I look in the mirror, I am disappointed by the color of my skin because I think that our society finds blonde-haired, blue-eyed girls more beautiful.

Sometimes I tell the people at Starbucks that my name is "Amy" so that they won't have to ask me 10 times how to spell my hard-to-pronounce, foreign name.

Sometimes I cringe at my relatives' thick Indian accents. Sometimes I make sure to invite my friends over before my mom cooks dinner so that the house doesn't smell like spices and curries.

Even in such a diverse place as the California Bay Area, a person can feel out of place and different from her peers. It helps me when I'm having a bad day, however, to remind myself that the people in my life who I love actually embrace all these things – my skin color, my name, my family member's accents, and the scent of my home.

These things make up a large part of my identity. I would never have guessed that my best friends would think that the food that stinks up my entire house smells delicious! They actually applauded my relatives for speaking English with excellent grammar, rather than scoffing at their unusual accents.

When I tell people stories about the meaning of my name, the numerous Indian holidays and festivals, or the mythical Hindu tales, they are engrossed and fascinated. This makes me even prouder of my background.

[...]

Extracted from: <www.pamf.org/teen/life/depression/normal-amerita.html>. Accessed on: Apr. 16, 2016.

2. Answer the following questions.

a. Where is Amrita's family from?

____

b. Where does she live?

____

c. Why does she tell people her name is Amy?

____

d. What does her mom use to spice the food?

____

3. Choose the correct alternative to answer the questions.

a. In the opinion of the author of the text, who does society find more beautiful?

- [ ] Blonde-haired, blue-eyed girls.
- [ ] Red-haired, brown-eyed girls.

b. Who doesn't mind her skin color, her accent and so on?

- [ ] Herself.
- [ ] The people she loves.

c. How good is her family's English?

- [ ] Fairly bad.
- [ ] Pretty good.

4. Read the first paragraph of the text again. Who do you think the author of the text refers to when she writes "our society"? Why?

____

____

5. Based on the text, do you think there is some kind of prejudice against Indian people in the United States? Research about it and confirm your answer.

____

____

____

6. Have you ever been in a situation someone was prejudiced against you or somebody you know? How did you feel? What can be done to change this?

____

____

____

7. Are there things that you don't like about yourself or about your family's traditions? Think about them. Why do they bother you and is there anything you can do to change them? Do you need to change them?

____

____

____

____

8. If you were a foreigner living in a very different country from yours, how do you think you would feel? If you were in trouble, who would you ask for advice?

____

____

____

____

UNIT 3 They fight to keep our planet healthy

Review the journey

1. Read the text. What is it?

a. ☐ An interview.   b. ☐ A comic strip.   c. ☐ A movie review.

www.vice.com/read/interview-with-the-warriors-of-aboriginal-resistance

We Interviewed Australia's Warriors of Aboriginal Resistance

By Courtney DeWitt

SCOTT BARBOUR/GETTY IMAGES

While most of the country's citizens marked Australia Day with barbecues and beer, on January 26 a large group of protesters gathered on the steps of the nation's parliamentary buildings to mourn the continents colonization by whites. There were several protests in Melbourne but one of the rowdiest came from the Warriors of Aboriginal Resistance, or WAR for short.

Launched before the G20 summit last November, WAR is a coalition of "young Aboriginal people committed to the cause of decolonization and Aboriginal Nationalism," as stated in its manifesto. Their #Genocidal20 protests last year saw 5,000 people marching through the streets of Brisbane before burning half a dozen Australian flags. We caught up with two of their members yesterday to ask about their provocative approach.

VICE: WAR is a powerful name. Can you tell me why you chose it?

MERIKI: It's no accident. We are Warriors of Aboriginal Resistance. Without resistance the white man succeeds in taking our land and country so our purpose is not to attack but defend and protect. We want to revive the warrior spirit in our people by facilitating a culture of resistance.

[...]

VICE: Okay so what does fighting look like? What is WAR's mission?

MERIKI: Decolonization. We want to inform our people and inspire them, particularly our youth, to take action in the anti-colonial struggle, because that's the only way. Decolonization encompasses all aspects of life. It's the food you eat, it's the things you buy. Food and health are high on our agenda, but we're also helping our own communities to learn their languages, their dances, the traditions. We want people to study and be informed of their true history.

to mourn: lamentar
the rowdiest: os mais expressivos
encompasses: engloba

Extracted from: <www.vice.com/read/interview-with-the-warriors-of-aboriginal-resistance>. Accessed on: Apr. 14, 2016.

BIS

2. Which pieces of information can we find in the text?

a. ☐ The place where the protesters met.

b. ☐ What the abbreviation WAR stands for.

c. ☐ Where the city of Brisbane is located.

d. ☐ How WAR was born.

e. ☐ Which activist groups are against colonization.

3. In the last paragraph there are two words in blue. Find and match them to the following definitions or synonyms.

a. the act of getting rid of colonization, or freeing a country from being dependent on another country: ______________________

b. fight: ______________________

4. Read the introduction again and underline the verbs in the past tense.

While most of the country's citizens marked Australia Day with barbecues and beer, on January 26 a large group of protesters gathered on the steps of the nation's parliamentary buildings to mourn the continents colonization by whites. There were several protests in Melbourne but one of the rowdiest came from the Warriors of Aboriginal Resistance, or WAR for short.

Launched before the G20 summit last November, WAR is a coalition of "young Aboriginal people committed to the cause of decolonization and Aboriginal Nationalism," as stated in its manifesto. Their #Genocidal20 protests last year saw 5,000 people marching through the streets of Brisbane before burning half a dozen Australian flags. We caught up with two of their members yesterday to ask about their provocative approach.

5. Rewrite the following sentences in the negative form.

a. They interviewed New Zealand's warriors of aboriginal resistance.

____

____

b. The group chose the name WAR by accident.

____

____

c. The protests saw 5,000 people marching through the streets of Brisbane.

____

____

d. We caught up with two of their members yesterday.

____

____

Another look

TEXT 1

1. Scan the text below and decide whether the sentences are **T** (true), **F** (false) or **NM** (not mentioned).

a. ☐ The text involves a process for obtaining information.

b. ☐ There is more than one person answering the questions.

c. ☐ Both people who are talking are taking turns.

d. ☐ The person who is asking the questions is recording the conversation.

Foreign Exchange Student Interviews – Marianne Aagesen

Question: Where did you come from, and what grade are you in?
Answer: I came from Kristiansand in Norway, and I'm a junior.
Question: What's the most different thing?
Answer: People here are much more open– they talk and say hi to each other; when you meet someone in the street, you would smile and say hi. The food is really different too, but I like it a lot better in Norway. I'm getting used to it though.
Question: Why did you decide to be a foreign exchange student?
Answer: A friend of my sister told me that she had the time of her life, and that inspired me to come here. She told me if I was thinking about it, I should do it, because it's only a year, and it's a once in a lifetime experience.
Question: What is your home like in Norway?
Answer: I live in a big house in Kristiansand, the weather is really different here. It changes really fast here.
Question: How is school different here?
Answer: The whole school system is different. We have one class in Norway that we stay in all the time. We don't get to choose classes. The teaching methods are the same. We have projects and we write essays, just like here.

ANTON JANKOVOY/SHUTTERSTOCK

Question: What's your favorite subject?
Answer: My favorite class is English, because I love Ms. Orwick. It's really fun. It was my favorite subject in Norway too.
Question: What's the hardest thing about being here?
Answer: The hardest thing is the insecurity, because when I came here I didn't know the personalities of the people I was going to live with. Here I'm all alone, and at home I had my sister and my mother with me all the time. Now I have to talk to people in English, and it's exhausting to have to translate in my head before I speak.
Question: What is the best thing about being here?
Answer: New experiences and being away from all the home drama. New friends.
Question: Would you recommend foreign exchange to someone else?
Answer: Oh yeah. Of course. Like I said, it's a once in a lifetime experience. And it's only a year out of all of the years that you live. It's a great experience. I would recommend that everybody do it! It's a whole new culture.

Extracted from: <https://bhsmaroontribune.com/2013/10/04/foreign-exchange-student-interviews-marianne-aagesen/>. Accessed on: Apr. 14, 2016.

2. Read the text. Conversations like the one we see in the text may happen between

a. ☐ a mother and a daughter.

b. ☐ an employer and a job applicant.

c. ☐ a singer and his old partner.

3. Read the text again and fill in the blanks with the appropriate information.

The exchange student believes that the people there are more ____________ than in Norway. However, she prefers the ____________ they make in her country. She also says this is a lifetime ____________. The weather in Norway doesn't ____________ fast and the whole school system is ____________ as well. One exhausting thing for her is having to speak in ____________ all the time.

4. What is the meaning of the expression **a lifetime experience**? Choose the correct alternative.

a. ☐ It is a not so good experience.

b. ☐ It is an experience that takes a lot of time to happen.

c. ☐ It is an experience that you will take with you for all your life.

d. ☐ It is an experience that ends with life.

5. Why does she recommend this experience?

____

____

____

1. Would you like to take part in an exchange experience? Where would you travel to? Why?

____

____

____

2. What other experiences do you think are lifetime experiences? Why?

____

____

____

TEXT 2

1. How often do you share meals with your friends and family?

____

____

2. Do you know traditional dishes from your city or state? What are they? Do you like them or not?

____

____

3. Read the text. What is its main subject?

____

____

www.allaboutcuisines.com/importance-food-preserving-cultural-identity

THE IMPORTANCE OF FOOD IN PRESERVING CULTURAL IDENTITY

[...]

Throughout most of history, bonds and shared cultures have been created when meals are prepared and shared. We need to bring the importance of community back into food. Our **heritage** is often passed down and intimately bound up in the food we eat. Food availability, climate and cooking techniques, evolved over many generations have united individuals and groups of people into a distinct culture.

If we do not take the time to teach the younger generations how to cook and interact with food they will not be able to engage with their culture and bond with the past. Sharing food and cooking techniques with family and friends gives them a chance to learn about your culture. Giving the cultures a taste, a smell, a feeling can increase respect and understanding between groups of people. The emotional impact that sharing food has on individuals, family or groups of people cannot be underestimated. The intimate first date, family celebration, business meal or a major festive event helps develop relationships and if combined with traditional food reinforces cultural identity.

Culture, emotions, and bonding are all integral parts of preparing and eating a meal. We are at risk that our busy lifestyle, work pressures and in some cases economic problems are causing us **to overlook** the importance of social eating. We need to make social eating more of a priority in our eating habits. The connections that food can create between people are too valuable to overlook.

> **heritage**: herança, patrimônio
> **to overlook**: ignorar

Extracted from: <www.allaboutcuisines.com/importance-food-preserving-cultural-identity>. Accessed on: Jun. 27, 2016.

4. Based on the text, explain the following sentences and write if you agree with them or not. Justify your answers.

a. "Our heritage is often passed down and intimately bound up in the food we eat."

____

____

____

b. "Giving the cultures a taste, a smell, a feeling can increase respect and understanding between groups of people."

____

____

____

c. "Culture, emotions, and bonding are all integral parts of preparing and eating a meal."

____

____

____

5. Which sentence is not correct according to the text?

a. ☐ Cooking and eating together is an important cultural element.

b. ☐ Knowledge about traditional cooking should be passed on to younger generations.

c. ☐ Cultural identity and traditional food do not have any relation between them.

d. ☐ The importance of traditional food and sharing meal times should not be forgotten.

1. What can you do to change your eating habits in order to share meals more frequently?

____

____

____

2. What can you do to help pass this cultural heritage on? Can you teach somebody how to cook something? Or is there anyone who can teach you how to cook?

____

____

____

Reading the world

1. Have you ever eaten food from any other country? Make a list of what you have already tried.

____

____

2. Now read the text. Have you ever tried this dish?

____

BIS

THINKSTOCK/GETTY IMAGES

www.foodbycountry.com/Germany-to-Japan/Jamaica.html

Food in Every Country

Jamaica

[...]

Before Christopher Columbus landed in Jamaica in 1492, the original inhabitants of the island were an Amerindian tribe called the Arawaks. They grew the spinach-like callaloo, papayas (which they called pawpaws), and guava. They also produced two crops each per year of maize (corn), potatoes, peanuts, peppers, and beans.

The Arawaks roasted seafood and meat on a grate suspended on four-forked sticks called a barbacoa, which is the origin of Western barbecue.

The closest neighboring Amerindian tribe was the Caribs, who were the most feared warriors of the Caribbean. They ate more simply than the Arawaks—mostly fish and peppers.

The Spanish invaded Jamaica, then called Xaymaca ("the land of wood and water") in the late 1400s. They were responsible for importing many of the plants for which Jamaica is now known, such as sugar cane, lemons, limes, and coconuts. They also imported pigs, cattle, and goats. The Spanish turned to trading slaves from Africa's West Coast for labor. The slaves brought with them ackee (a tropical tree with edible fruit, now the national fruit of Jamaica), okra, peanuts, and a variety of peas and beans, all considered staples in the modern-day Jamaica.

Jamaica is now an English-speaking country, although it has a Creole dialect called Patois, which is influenced mostly by West African languages. Ninety-five per cent of the population is of partial or total African descent. Nearly the whole population is native-born Jamaican.

Rice and Peas

Kidney beans may be substituted for Jamaican peas (usually pigeon peas).

Ingredients

- 1 cup canned red kidney beans
- 2 cups rice
- 1 cup coconut milk
- 4 cups water
- 1 stalk of fresh thyme, finely chopped (or 2 teaspoons dried)
- 2 green onions, chopped
- ½ cup onion, chopped
- Hot pepper flakes, to taste
- Salt and pepper, to taste

SIMON REDDY/ALAMY/FOTOARENA

Procedure

1. Combine beans, water, coconut milk, thyme, green onions, and onions over medium heat until just boiling.
2. Add salt, pepper, and hot pepper flakes to taste.
3. Add rice, cover, and simmer over low heat for 25 minutes until rice is tender and liquids have been absorbed. Check after 15 minutes and add more water if necessary.
4. Serve warm.

Extracted from: <www.foodbycountry.com/Germany-to-Japan/Jamaica.html>. Accessed on: Apr. 15, 2016.

3. Match the names of food to the pictures.

a. spinach

b. guava

c. peas

d. kidney beans

e. thyme

f. pepper flakes

THINKSTOCK/GETTY IMAGES

THINKSTOCK/GETTY IMAGES

THINKSTOCK/GETTY IMAGES

THINKSTOCK/GETTY IMAGES

THINKSTOCK/GETTY IMAGES

THINKSTOCK/GETTY IMAGES

4. Find in the text.

a. the name of a tribe: ______________________

b. an English word for "pawpaw": ______________________

c. another word for "corn": ______________________

d. a native language spoken in Jamaica: ______________________

e. a word for "suitable to be eaten": ______________________

f. an equivalent to "cooked (food, especially meat) by prolonged exposure to heat in an oven or over a fire": ______________________

5. Would you like to try this Rice and Peas dish? Do you think you can make it?

____

____

6. What's your favorite dish? Can you name its ingredients?

____

____

UNIT 4

Has the music industry changed?

Review the journey

1. Unscramble the words and complete with **some**-, **any**- or **no**- compounds to make sentences.

a. said / start / concert / the / ______________ / about / is / to

____

b. ______________ / do / that / know / you / about / ?

____

c. didn't / ______________ / see / I / there

____

d. shower / is / there / than / better / going / ______________ / before / bed / to / taking / a

____

2. Check the alternative that completes the conversation properly.

a. **A:** What do you usually do on weekends?

B: ☐ Well, I always try to do something interesting on weekends. I go to the theater, to the movies, to museums or art galleries. I also go to parks or other open air events. There is never a weekend that I only stay home.

B: ☐ Well, I always try to do anything interesting on weekends. There isn't nothing that I don't like doing, so there is always something for me.

b. **A:** Can you tell me where the supermarket is?

B: I'm sorry, but there are no supermarkets around here. What do you need?

A: ☐ Oh, really? Well, that's OK. It was nothing really important.

A: ☐ Oh, really? Well, where can I buy nothing to drink around here?

c. **A:** I need help tiding up my bedroom. It is such a mess. Do you have some time to help me so I can finish it faster?

B: ☐ Well, I'm sorry, but there isn't nothing I can do. It is your bedroom and you have to be responsible for it.

B: ☐ Well, I'm sorry, but there is nothing I can do. It is your bedroom and you have to be responsible for it.

3. Answer the questions.

a. Who did you use to talk to when you needed help with your homework?

____

b. Who used to be your best friend in first grade? Are you still in touch with this person?

____

c. Where did you use to go to when you were on vacation?

____

4. Complete the table below with the names of artists you like.

My preferences						
	National artists			International artists		
Jazz						
Electronic						
Rock						
Country						
Rap						
Pop						
Classical						

5. Talk to a classmate about your list. Share your preferences and ask about his/hers, then complete the following table and see if you have similar musical preferences.

My classmate's preferences						
	National artists			International artists		
Jazz						
Electronic						
Rock						
Country						
Rap						
Pop						
Classical						

Another look

TEXT 1

1. Take a look at the text below and choose the correct answer.

a. The text is

☐ descriptive and little informative. ☐ informative and visually stimulating.

b. It contains

☐ rhymes and imagery. ☐ statistics and data.

c. It

☐ highlights some information. ☐ hides significant information.

d. Its target audience would most probably be

☐ musicians. ☐ roadies.

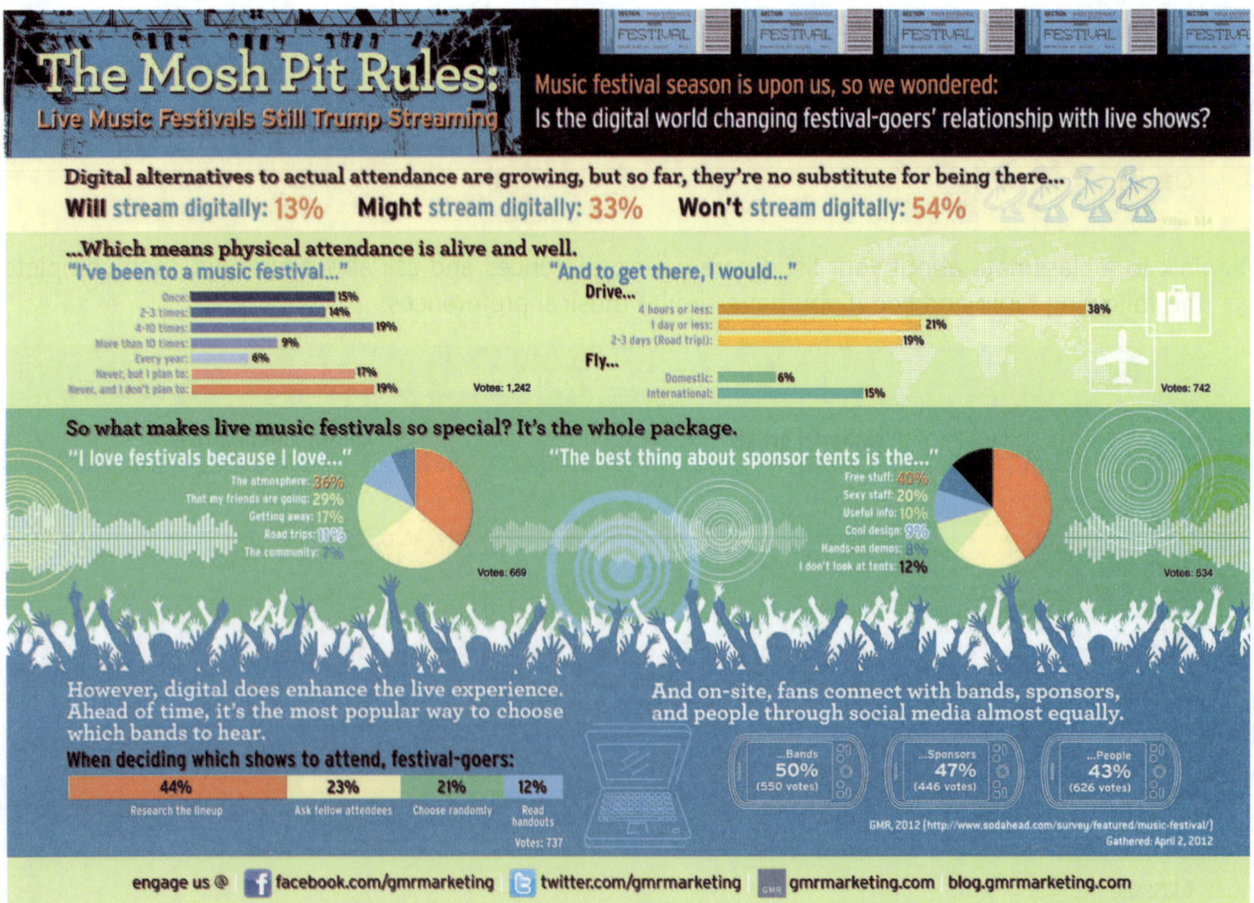

GMR MARKETING/WWW.GMRMARKETING.COM

2. Read the text and use the words from the box to complete the paragraph.

audience's relationship	more connected	music festivals	music lovers	this infographic

The main goal of ____________________ is to inform the audience about live ____________________. They question whether the digital world is changing the ____________________ with live shows. According to the graphic, the digital world may help ____________________ decide which shows they want to see. And it also helps them become ____________________ with the bands.

3. Use words from the infographic to complete the sentences.

a. Digital alternatives are not a __________ for fans not to go to a show.

b. Nine percent of the people interviewed have been to a music festival more than ten __________.

c. To get to a festival, most interviewees would __________ four hours or less.

d. Most of them enjoy festivals because of the __________.

4. Match the answers to the questions.

a. How much percent of the people interviewed will not stream digitally?

b. How much percent attend a live festival every year?

c. How much percent love festivals because of the road trips?

☐ Six percent.

☐ Eleven percent.

☐ Fifty-four percent.

1. Now talk about your own experience with downloading music or streaming music services. Which do you prefer? Why?

____

____

2. If you could choose, would you watch a live show by streaming or by being there? Why?

____

____

3. Do you follow artists you like on social medias? Why?

____

____

TEXT 2

1. Scan the text and check the correct answers.

a. In "Musician Jason Isbell says Web streaming 'doesn't add to my income in any way.'", **in any way** may be substituted by

- [ ] anyway.
- [ ] in any matter.

b. Another way of saying "But musicians and songwriters say they're barely seeing any money from streaming" is

- [ ] But musicians and songwriters say they're seeing almost no money from streaming.
- [ ] But musicians and songwriters say they're seeing some money from streaming.

Songwriters: Spotify doesn't pay off... unless you're a Taylor Swift

Musician Jason Isbell says Web streaming "doesn't add to my income in any way."

THINKSTOCK/GETTY IMAGES

(CNN) If you listen to rock or pop, you've heard Desmond Child's work.

And if you were one of the 6.5 million people who listened to Bon Jovi's "Livin' on a Prayer" on Pandora during a three-month span in 2012, you helped him, and his two co-writers, split a grand total of $110.

"We could each buy a pizza," said Child, an inductee in the Songwriters Hall of Fame who has worked with artists ranging from Aerosmith and Kiss to Ricky Martin and Cher. "A large pizza."

Music streaming apps and sites were supposed to make music cheap – or free – for consumers while assuring that the artists who created the songs would be fairly compensated.

But musicians and songwriters say they're barely seeing any money from streaming.

"It's upside down," Child said. "It needs to get back in balance. It's just simply not fair."

Last week, singer Taylor Swift pulled all of her music from Spotify, saying that the ability to stream her new album, "1989," threatened to hurt sales. Spotify has roughly 50 million users, who either pay $9.99 a month for the service or listen to a free version with advertisements.

"I'm glad the Taylor Swift thing has caused people to consider it more, because I do think it's an imperfect business model," said Jason Isbell, the Americana Music Association's 2014 Artist of the Year, whose albums are available on the streaming sites.

The Taylor Swifts of the world can actually make out well on streaming sites – Spotify said she had been on pace to make $6 million from the app this year. But Isbell said he earns so little in online streaming royalties that he barely pays attention to them.

"It doesn't add to my income in any way that isn't negligible," he said.

[...]

unless: a não ser que
span: período
split: dividirem
roughly: aproximadamente
negligible: insignificante

Extracted from: <http://edition.cnn.com/2014/11/12/tech/web/spotify-pay-musicians/>. Accessed on: Apr. 15, 2016.

2. Read the text and use the words from the box to complete the sentences.

used to be	used to earn	used to publish

GARETH CATTERMOLE/TAS/GETTY IMAGES

a. Bon Jovi's "Livin' on a prayer" ________________ a hit.

b. Country pop singer Taylor Swift ________________ her music on Spotify.

c. Artists ________________ more money in the past.

3. Read the title of the text again: "Songwriters: Spotify doesn't pay off... unless you're a Taylor Swift".

a. What is the meaning of **pay off**?

____

____

b. Why does it mention Taylor Swift?

____

____

c. How much did the songwriter mentioned in the text earn for "Livin' on a prayer", by Bon Jovi?

____

____

4. Write **T** (true) or **F** (false).

a. ☐ Artists want to end streaming services.

b. ☐ Taylor Swift earns a lot of money from streaming services and that's why she defends them.

c. ☐ Streaming services, such as Spotify, are paid for or free, but with advertisement.

d. ☐ Desmond Child made millions from streaming services.

e. ☐ Jason Isbell thinks streaming services are not profitable for artists who are not as famous as Taylor Swift.

1. How much do you think is a fair price to pay for a song?

____

____

2. Is it easy to stablish prices for cultural goods? Why?

____

____

Reading the world

1. Do you know of a period in Brazilian history when certain lyrics were censored? How do you feel about censorship? Explain it. Then read the text. Did your opinion about censorship change?

Three years in prison for simply singing a wrong song

[...]

"Normally, concerts in North Korea are limited to performances of music that [the country's leader] Kim Jong-il himself is (falsely) credited with having written or at least approved. Merely to listen to radio broadcasts from other nations is to risk imprisonment. During a party on Christmas in 1992, one of the regime's former propaganda officers, Ji Hae Nam, made the mistake of singing a South Korean song. She was sentenced to three years in jail and, as she testified to the United States Congress after her escape, beaten so severely she could not get up for a month," wrote Richard V. Allen, co-chairman of the United States Committee for Human Rights in North Korea, in New York Times on 28 October 2007.

The North Korean government encourages light, state-sponsored music, or music with patriotic worker-driven themes played on radios or in public by large worker's orchestras. Kim Jong-il only permits music that sing the praises of his every move, or otherwise the ideals of communism, and songs have titles like 'Our Life Is Precisely a Song', 'We Shall Hold Bayonettes More Firmly' and 'The Joy of Bumper Harvest Overflows Amidst the Song of Mechanisation'.

CNN interview in 2008

On the occasion of New York Philharmonic's concert in North Korea on 26 February 2008, CNN's star reporter Christiane Amanpour travelled to South Korea to meet the exiled singer. Amanpour's report was aired on 11 May 2008, and CNN has published the following transcript of the TV interview on their website, transcripts.cnn.com:

JI HAE NAM, NORTH KOREAN DEFECTOR (through translator):

"In North Korea, you have been brainwashed since you were young. You can only sing songs about the party, Kim Il-Sung and [his son] Kim Jong-il."

CHRISTIANE AMANPOUR (voice over):

For 15 years, her government job was to spread the word of Kim Il-Sung and Kim Jong-il through song. But it never occurred to Ji that singing a song in the privacy of her own home would be considered a crime.

HAE NAM (through translator):

"I sang a South Korean song."

AMANPOUR (on camera):

"And what happened when you got caught?"

HAE NAM (through translator):

"I was interrogated for five months. I was sentenced to jail."

AMANPOUR (voice over):

She says she was starved and tortured for three years.

(On camera):

"All of this for singing an unsanctioned Korean folk song?"

HAE NAM (through translator):

"I was charged with a crime of spreading punk ideology to a healthy society. "

AMANPOUR (voice over):

Ji Hae Nam was released from prison in 1995 and made a desperate escape to China. She eventually found her way to South Korea, where today, 13 years later, nobody could be more amazed about what's about to happen just 150 miles north in Pyongyang...

In February 2008, North Korea was putting on its best face for its American guests, the New York Philharmonic. When they performed in the capital Pyongyang, they were "bridging a divide between the United States and North Korea which is based on hatred, fear and ignorance," said Christiane Amanpour, who ended her CNN-report with these words: "For a few hours at least, these sworn enemies shared the love of beautiful music, and the hope perhaps that a few notes might signal a new beginning."

[...]

Extracted from: <http://freemuse.org/archives/1254>. Accessed on: Apr. 15, 2016.

2. Which words have a positive connotation and which have a negative connotation?

brainwashed hatred healthy praise wrong

Positive	Negative

3. Match questions and answers.

a. How long was Ji Hae Nam sentenced to jail?
b. How long did she work for the government?
c. When was she freed?
d. When did CNN's reporter Christiane Amanpour interview Ji Hae Nam?

☐ In 2008.
☐ Fifteen years.
☐ Three years.
☐ In 1995.

4. Check the reason why Ji Hae Nam was sent to prison.

a. ☐ Her songs were broadcasted on the radio.
b. ☐ She sang a South Korean song.
c. ☐ She was spreading communist ideology.
d. ☐ She was opposed to the North Korean government.

5. What was the event that happened in 2008 described in the article? According to Christiane Amanpour, what could be the role of music in that event? Do you agree with the journalist about that?

____

____

____

____

6. Do you know examples of countries that censor the internet and artistic manifestations? How do you feel about that? Justify your answer.

____

____

____

____

UNIT

5 No more

Review the journey

1. Read the following sentences and put the linking words or expressions in bold in the correct column.

a. We had several meetings **in order to** organize our school work.

b. Students **as well as** teachers are responsible for education.

c. The last political debate didn't come to a conclusion, **thus**, another debate will be scheduled soon.

d. **All in all**, we must focus on what happens around us, **so** that we won't let anything wrong happen.

e. **Despite** all the hard work, rebuilding this square was worth it. **For this reason**, today we celebrate!

f. I will not travel tonight **since** it is raining. **Besides**, the traffic is too heavy, as we have a holiday tomorrow.

g. **Although** slavery was abolished many years ago, we have cases of modern slavery that must be taken care of.

addition	contrast	reason	conclusion	effect

2. Now choose the correct linking word or expression from the table in activity 1 to complete the sentences below.

a. ____________________ exercise ____________________ save some money, we always walk to school.

b. The plot was not the most surprising. The soundtrack was perfect, ____________________ being very innovative, it gave the movie a great atmosphere. Photography was great, too, ____________________ some few scenes that were too dark. ____________________, it was a nice movie.

c. There was not enough food for everybody, ____________________, people complained a lot about the party.

d. ____________________ I do not have enough time, I suggest we continue this conversation tomorrow.

3. Use the verbs given in the correct form.

COMSTOCK IMAGES/GETTY IMAGES

If I could, I would change certain things at home. I'm sure my parents would have more free time if they ____________ (find) a job close to where we live. If we ____________ (live) close to their present jobs, we would not be able to have such a big house or apartment. As we have two dogs, if we ____________ (move) to an apartment, we would need to find a new place for them, but none of us want that. If we ____________ (have not) pets, maybe we could move.

4. Read the conditions below and write what would happen in each situation. If you don't know the respective fairy tale, look for it on the internet or talk to your friends about it.

a. What would happen if Snow White didn't bite the poisoned apple?

____

____

b. What would happen if Little Red Riding Hood's grandmother didn't let the Big Bad Wolf in?

____

____

c. What would happen if the Hare didn't sleep while running against the Tortoise?

____

____

d. What would happen if all three little pigs made houses with bricks?

____

____

e. What would happen if Cinderella's stepmother was good to her?

____

____

f. What would happen if Hansel and Gretel could find their way back home from the woods for the second time?

____

____

Another look

TEXT 1

1. Read the title of the text. How would you explain this affirmation?

Discriminating against women keeps countries poorer

In 100 countries around the world, women are barred from doing certain work solely because they are women. More than 150 countries have at least one law that is discriminatory towards women. And only 18 countries are free of any law disadvantaging women.

This is just the tip of the iceberg of legal barriers for women to achieve their full economic potential. New World Bank Group research in the Women, Business and the Law 2016 report shows that in 32 countries women cannot apply for passports in the same way as men and in 18 countries they cannot get a job if their husbands feel it is not in the family's interest. Jordan and Iran are among them. In 59 countries, there are no laws against sexual harassment at work. Myanmar, Uzbekistan and Armenia are among 46 countries where there is no legal protection against domestic violence. In a nutshell, the research makes for depressing reading when you care about inclusion and ending poverty.

Countries whose laws discriminate against women and do not promote gender equality suffer economically. Previous research tells us that gender gaps in women's entrepreneurship and labor force participation account for estimated income losses of 27% in the Middle East and North Africa, 19% in South Asia, 14% in Latin America and the Caribbean and 10% in Europe. These are losses that many countries can't afford, particularly those facing high levels of poverty.

There is good news too: Countries like Bangladesh are encouraging female participation in the workforce. If they stay on track, their female workforce will grow from 34 to 82% over the next decade, adding 1.8 percentage points to their GDP. In the 1990s very few countries had laws protecting women from violence, now 127 do partially because the world is more aware of the human and economic cost of mistreating women.

When women are allowed to work in a profession of their choice, when they have access to financial services and when they are protected, by law, from domestic violence, they are not only economically empowered, they also live longer. The more say they have over the household income and the more they participate in the economy, the more girls are enrolled in secondary school, the larger the benefits for their children, their communities, and their countries. In fact, every additional year of primary school boosts girls' eventual wages by 10 to 20%, and an extra year of secondary school by 15 to 25%.

[...]

JOERG BOETHLING/ALAMY/FOTOAREANA

GDP: *Gross domestic product*
(PIB: Produto Interno Bruto)

Extracted from: <http://blogs.worldbank.org/voices/discriminating-against-women-keeps-countries-poorer>. Accessed on: Apr. 18, 2016.

2. Read the text and write **T** (true), **F** (false) or **NM** (not mentioned).

a. ☐ In a small number of countries, there are laws that discriminate against women.

b. ☐ In some countries, women cannot even apply for passports in the same way as men.

c. ☐ In Bangladesh women are not part of the workforce.

d. ☐ In Iran there is no legal protection against domestic violence.

e. ☐ In Jordan, for instance, a woman depends on her husband's approval if she wants to have a job.

3. Match the columns to make sentences.

a. If some women didn't have a job,

b. If a country like Bangladesh stays on track,

c. If a country doesn't promote gender equality,

d. In certain countries, if there were no laws against sexual harassment at work,

☐ women would feel humiliated.

☐ their families could suffer.

☐ its female workforce will grow from 34 to 82% over the next decade.

☐ its economy will be poorer.

4. What are the worrying points the text shows about gender gap? And what has improved over the years, according to the text? Mention at least three items in each column.

Worrying points	Improvements

1. How do you think women are treated in Brazil? Is it the same as men? Compare the answers among boys and girls in your classroom. Do you have the same opinion?

___

___

2. What can you do to decrease the gender gap in your community?

___

___

TEXT 2

1. Observe the picture below. The text is most probably about

a. ☐ maps. b. ☐ traveling. c. ☐ statistics.

2. Take a quick look at the text.

a. Find a quote.

b. Is it a formal or informal text?

BIS

https://livelytwist.com/2016/03/13/blogging-109-word-travel-combating-prejudice/

Blogging 109… Word Travel: combating prejudice

MARCH 13, 2016 ~ LIVELYTWIST

1 Mark Twain's quote from his book, *The Innocents Abroad*, rings true.

> "Travel is fatal to prejudice, bigotry, and narrow-mindedness, and many of our people need it sorely on these accounts. Broad, wholesome, charitable views of men and things cannot be acquired by vegetating in one little corner of the earth all one's lifetime."

2 My travels overseas have shown me how little people know about Nigeria and the African continent and revealed my prejudice and penchant for stereotypes. If you never travel and watch only one TV channel, you may conclude that Europe is awash with refugees, America with gun violence, the Middle East with terrorism, and Africa with war, poverty, and disease.

3 But hopping on a plane, train, or bus and going miles and miles away from home can be expensive. However, we're not limited by budget if we can read. Literacy and internet access provide cheaper alternatives to confront narrow-mindedness.

4 Like most of my friends, I remember travelling to faraway places as a girl through the books I read. The writers stimulated our senses as we journeyed with them, so we were familiar not only with the sights, sounds, and smells of places, but also with their peoples and culture. […]

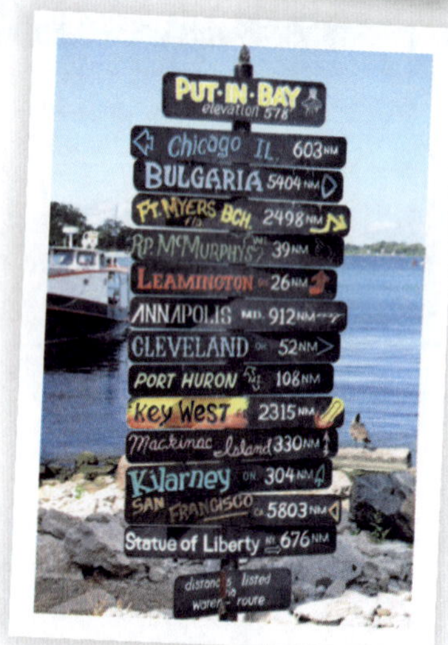

ISTOCKPHOTO/GETTY IMAGES

bigotry: intolerância
penchant: propensão, inclinação
awash: cheia, inundada

Extracted from: <https://livelytwist.com/2016/03/13/blogging-109-word-travel-combating-prejudice/>. Accessed on: Apr. 18, 2016.

3. Read the text and check.

a. ☐ It is an infographic. b. ☐ It is a blog entry. c. ☐ It is a biography.

4. In which paragraph can you find the following subjects?

a. [ ] How well people from other continents know Africa.

b. [ ] The blogger's childhood.

c. [ ] What people in general think of the Middle East.

d. [ ] Alternatives to get better informed.

5. Use the words from the box to complete the sentences.

apps	blog	post (2x)	updated

a. If you want to share ideas, experiences and/or photos, videos, etc. with your friends and family, you can write a ____________________.

b. Blogs are online journals that are frequently ____________________.

c. An update is also called an entry or a ____________________.

d. When you ____________________ something, the readers can respond online.

e. Nowadays it is also possible to send messages or share short videos through ____________________.

1. Do you agree that blogs (and instant message apps) are great to keep everyone in a family, for example, up-to-date with the latest news?

____

____

____

2. How do you prefer to keep in touch with others? Explain your reasons.

____

____

____

3. Do you write a blog yourself? If not, would you like to? Why?

____

____

____

Reading the world

1. Read the posters. What do they have in common?

BACK SPIN DESIGN/ARQUIVO PESSOAL

ADRIANA DE BARROS/PROJECT 1210

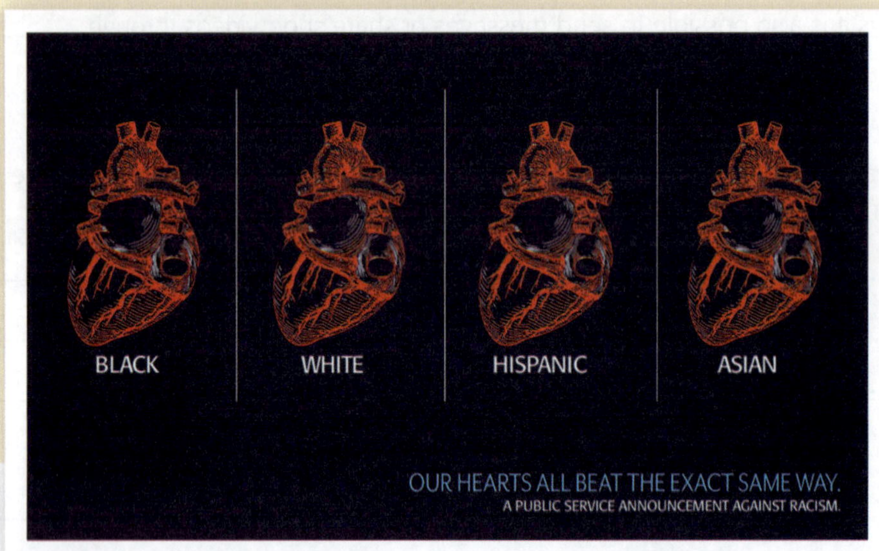

LYNDI MUNGUIA/WWW.BEHANCE.NET/LYNDIMAY

____

____

2. In your opinion, which poster is the most impressive? Why?

____

____

3. Now read the stories below and complete the sentences.

Your Stories of Racism: Beyond Black and White

I am an Indian-American living in Arkansas. A Hispanic store employee yelled at me "I don't know whatever the hell you are saying," then stared at me real long and asked "Do you even speak English?" I was on my way to celebrate my 1,000th day in the US! I was working as a logistics engineer, having recently graduated with a master's in industrial engineering.

I am half Japanese and half Malaysian-Chinese. I have big, round eyes. People assume that I'm "half-Asian" and they fetishise me. But when I correct them, their faces fall almost into a grimace and say "well, at least your eyes aren't too Asian," as if I was lucky not to look Asian because being Asian is bad enough. The difference between racism towards Asians and racism towards other races is that everyday people, even educated people who fight against racism, think that it's okay to say these things, to point out these supposed faults of being Asian as part of quotidian conversation.

Adapted from: <www.theatlantic.com/national/archive/2015/07/racism-stories-beyond-black-white-ta-nehisi-coates/398561/>. Accessed on: Apr. 19, 2016.

a. The first report is about ______________________________.

b. The second report is about ______________________________.

4. Answer the following questions based on the texts.

a. Why did the employee yell at the customer?

____

____

b. How long had the customer been living in the US?

____

____

c. What do the people who said "at least your eyes aren't too Asian" most probably think of the shape of Asian eyes?

____

____

d. What do some people think it's OK to say?

____

____

5. Is there discrimination against foreigners in your country? If the answer is yes, give one or two examples. What can you do to change this reality?

____

____

____

UNIT 6

To buy or not to buy

Review the journey

1. Match the types of advertising to their definitions.

a. online advertising
b. print advertising
c. guerrilla advertising
d. broadcast advertising
e. public service advertising
f. outdoor advertising
g. cell phone advertising
h. product placement advertising

☐ As most cell phones now have internet connectivity and operational systems that allow the use of apps, there is advertising being made to be displayed on the apps.

☐ When you visit a website, there might be sponsored content, banners or other kinds of advertising. This is the main source of income for website owners.

☐ When a TV show or movie shows a product, maybe consuming it, or mentioning a brand.

☐ This kind of advertising is designed to inform and educate people, instead of selling something. It is used to promote campaigns and ideas that are of public interest.

☐ It is a type of advertisement that is unconventional, usually requiring consumer to interact with it, or displayed in an unconventional place. Creative ideas and innovation are the driving forces in this type of advertising.

☐ Any kind of advertising that reaches consumers when they are not in their houses. So, it is a big category in which we can find billboards, for example.

☐ All advertisement that is printed on paper, be it newspapers, magazines, flyers, or anything else that is a portable printed medium.

☐ All advertisement that is shown on TV or on the radio.

2. Complete the sentences with the corresponding tag question.

a. Outdoor advertising is not the same thing as online advertising, ________________?

b. Advertising can be very interesting, ________________?

c. People usually remember catchy phrases in advertisement, ________________?

d. You have already worked at advertising agencies, ________________?

e. She is going to buy her apartment this month, ________________?

f. He planned a very successful piece of advertisement, ________________?

3. Look at the pictures and identify them according to the types of advertisement in activity 1.

a. 

MIKE SUKLE/SUKLE ADVERTISING & DESIGN, DENVER, USA

d. 
S.BORISOV/SHUTTERSTOCK

b. 

IB BORUP/BATES YR, COPENHAGEN, DENMARK

e. 
©WARNER BROS/COURTESY EVERETT COLLECTION/AGB PHOTO

c. 
©COLUMBIA PICTURES/COURTESY EVERETT COLLECTION/AGB PHOTO

f. 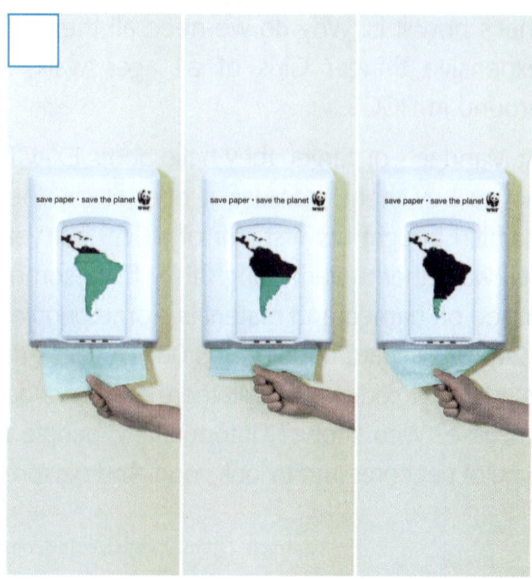

SIMON WOOLLER/SAATCHI & SAATCHI, COPENHAGEN, DENMARK/WWF

Another look

TEXT 1

1. How often do you buy clothes? How do you choose the clothes you buy?

____

____

2. When talking about clothes, do you have a favorite brand? Why is that your favorite?

____

____

3. Read the text. Does it mention any brands?

____

____

Label Me

OLENA ZASKOCHENKO/SHUTTERSTOCK

For years now, name brands have become more and more popular – as well as expensive. In my high school, I see several students in the hallways with extremely high-priced clothing, jewelry, etc. I'll be honest, it disgusts me. Our parents/ guardians have hard-working jobs and most of the things you get are coming from your parents/guardians salary. Is that fair? When you become their age, would you like it if your children spent YOUR money? Because that's how it is. Why do we need all these expensive things? Girls of all ages walk around in UGGS.

At Mandee's or Target, they have boots EXACTLY like UGGS, but we choose not to buy them, because it doesn't say the name-brand stamped on the bottom/back of the boots. I'll admit, I bought my first pair of UGGS last year with my own money that I EARNED from babysitting; and I still wear them even though they have some wear-and-tear on them. Let's face it, society is very much so based on namebrand materials. Some people just cannot afford these expensive things. Since when are shirts $24.99? Why are hoodies $45.00? Do jeans really need to be priced at $50.00? Is it fair? Of course not. Will there ever be a decrease in prices? Will there be an increase? Who knows? Unfortunately, people nowadays have to cope with this type of peer pressure to look good. And personally, I'm blind-sided to really... why?

wear-and-tear: desgastes, deterioração
blind-sided: chocada

Extracted from: <www.teenink.com/opinion/pop_culture_trends/article/63529/Label-Me/>. Accessed on: Apr. 20, 2016.

4. Find in the first paragraph a word or expression that means:

a. products or items made by a famous maker or manufacturer, as opposed to by a generic manufacturer: ____________________

b. expensive: ____________________

c. reasonable; rational: ____________________

5. Copy from the second paragraph sentences or parts of sentences that answer the questions.

a. When did you buy your first pair of UGGS?

____

b. How did you earn the money to buy them?

____

c. What can't some people do?

____

6. What is the main idea of this text?

____

____

7. Complete the sentences with tag questions.

a. Name brands have become more and more popular, ____________________?

b. Our parents/guardians have hard-working jobs, ____________________?

c. It doesn't matter if the name brand isn't stamped on your clothes, ____________________?

d. Society is very much so based on name brand materials, ____________________?

8. Now, answer the questions in activity 7 and justify your answers.

a. ____________________

b. ____________________

c. ____________________

d. ____________________

1. Do you think the situation reported in the text happens in your school, too?

____

____

2. How do you feel about the price of clothes? Do you think about the price before you buy something?

____

____

TEXT 2

1. Observe the comic strip below and choose the correct answers.

   a. The images are arranged
      - [ ] horizontally.
      - [ ] vertically.

   b. The narrative is presented in a
      - [ ] non-chronological sequence.
      - [ ] chronological sequence.

   c. Most of the lines are inside
      - [ ] boxes.
      - [ ] speech bubbles.

   d. This type of text is intended to be
      - [ ] humorous.
      - [ ] neutral.

   e. Such material is often printed in a
      - [ ] magazine.
      - [ ] brochure.

2. Read the comic strip and complete the sentences about it.

STONE SOUP **BY JAN ELIOT**

a. The mother doesn't agree the program she was watching was a ______________ program.

b. She complains the program was all about crime and there were lots of ______________.

c. She seems to be concerned about issues like the ______________, global warming, and race relations.

d. She adds that the world is ruled by materialism and ______________.

3. Write **T** (true) or **F** (false).

a. ☐ Holly was watching the TV news with her mother.

b. ☐ Holly's mother expected news about different subjects.

c. ☐ The news showed only crime reports.

d. ☐ Holly's mother liked the amount of advertisement she saw.

e. ☐ Holly wanted to discuss about the spiritual vacuum her mother mentioned.

4. What is Holly's answer to her mother's complaints?

____

5. Based on her suggestion, do you think Holly is concerned about the issues her mother pointed out? Is she aware of what materialism and consumerism mean?

____

____

6. How would you define the following words? Use a dictionary to help you if necessary.

a. materialism: ______________________________

____

b. consumerism: ______________________________

____

c. vacuum: ______________________________

____

1. Do you think TV news in Brazil are the same as the one Holly and her mother watched? Why?

____

____

2. What do you think about the issues Holly's mother talked about? Are we ruled by materialism and consumerism? What can you do to make people aware of this?

____

____

Reading the world

1. When it comes to buying, check the alternatives that describe your behavior.

a. ☐ I usually buy things I don't need.

b. ☐ I usually choose expensive brands.

c. ☐ I don't know the name of famous brands.

d. ☐ I buy something new every week.

2. Do you think Brazilian consumers are similar to Japanese consumers? Why? Read the text and check your answers.

____

____

____

The Japanese Consumer Mindset

First of all, you must understand the traditional "Japanese Consumer Mindset"!

[...]

1 Walking in the Akihabara area (the town of electronics shops in central Tokyo), you will notice the appetite of Japanese consumers for new gadgets, new products and new technologies. This is true for other product lines too, to a lower extent maybe. It is considered as fashionable to own the latest model, whatever the price of it.

[...]

2 When it comes to quality, Japanese are said to be the most demanding customers. The reason is that quality evaluation does not end with the Product: it includes service during the sales process and also after-sales service!!! Overstaffing in department stores derives from the same notion: there should always be a member of staff available nearby, even in case of sudden high affluence.

EASY CAMERA/SHUTTERSTOCK

3 Consumers in Japan value brand information, service, delivery, packaging & advertising as important factors in assessing quality & in making purchase decisions. Brand orientation is important as it conveys a double message of social status and insurance of quality.

[...]

4 Shopping in Japan can be considered as an alternative to "going out to see a show" or to "home entertainment". Among typical activities of young "Office Ladies", we have Shopping with friends and teatime (famous "cake set") on Saturday afternoons.

[...]

5 The price range of the purchased goods often varies from the lowest (for practical use) to the highest (for social status). Imported brands from the West, sold at high prices, contrast with the expansion of 100JPY shops and other types of low-price retailers. For luxury purchases, Japanese are willing to pay a premium price for all the extra costs related to the above described high quality standards & service expectations.

[...]

mindset: mentalidade
retailers: varejistas

Extracted from: <www.linkedin.com/pulse/japanese-consumer-mindset-philippe-huysveld-ir-mba>. Accessed on: Apr. 20, 2016.

3. In which paragraphs can we find these pieces of information?

a. ☐ Quality of services in Japanese department stores.

b. ☐ What is fashionable to possess in Japan.

c. ☐ Where their imported brands come from.

d. ☐ When the famous "cake set" is held.

e. ☐ What brand orientation involves.

4. Talk about your shopping habits. Answer the questions.

a. How often do you go shopping?

b. Where do you prefer to buy clothes, accessories, etc.?

c. Do you like brand clothes? Do you have any favorite brand?

5. Choose one of the topics below and try to defend it.

- Advertising influences shoppers' habits in a bad way.
- Certain ads should be banned.
- Ads do not help people decide which products are the best.

6. Read the following ad. What is your opinion about it?

PATTY ORLANDO/ART DIRECTOR

UNIT 7 Understanding children's rights

Review the journey

1. Do you know how an official law or declaration is structured? Match the terms from the box to their definitions.

article	item	paragraph	preamble

a. ______________________: a distinct often numbered or otherwise designated section of a document or writing (as a statute or pleading)

b. ______________________: a separate part of a legal document that deals with a single subject

c. ______________________: a statement that is made at the beginning of something (such as a legal document) and usually gives the reasons for the parts that follow

d. ______________________: a distinct part in an enumeration, account, or series

Extracted from: <www.merriam-webster.com/>. Accessed on: Jun. 6, 2016.

2. Identify the elements from activity 1 in the following text.

Convention on the Rights of the Child

____

The States Parties to the present Convention,

Considering that, in accordance with the principles proclaimed in the Charter of the United Nations, recognition of the inherent dignity and of the equal and inalienable rights of all members of the human family is the foundation of freedom, justice and peace in the world,

ONU - ORGANIZAÇÃO DAS NAÇÕES UNIDAS/ARQUIVO DA EDITORA

Bearing in mind that the peoples of the United Nations have, in the Charter, reaffirmed their faith in fundamental human rights and in the dignity and worth of the human person, and have determined to promote social progress and better standards of life in larger freedom,

[...]

Bearing in mind that the need to extend particular care to the child has been stated in the Geneva Declaration of the Rights of the Child of 1924 and in the Declaration of the Rights of the Child adopted by the General Assembly on 20 November 1959 and recognized in the Universal Declaration of Human Rights, in the International Covenant on Civil and Political Rights (in particular in articles 23 and 24), in the International Covenant on

Economic, Social and Cultural Rights (in particular in article 10) and in the statutes and relevant instruments of specialized agencies and international organizations concerned with the welfare of children,
Bearing in mind that, as indicated in the Declaration of the Rights of the Child, "the child, by reason of his physical and mental immaturity, needs special safeguards and care, including appropriate legal protection, before as well as after birth",
[...]
Recognizing the importance of international co-operation for improving the living conditions of children in every country, in particular in the developing countries,
Have agreed as follows:

PART I

[...]

________________ 13

________________ 1. The child shall have the right to freedom of expression; this right shall include freedom to seek, receive and impart information and ideas of all kinds, regardless of frontiers, either orally, in writing or in print, in the form of art, or through any other media of the child's choice.

________________ 2. The exercise of this right may be subject to certain restrictions, but these shall only be such as are provided by law and are necessary:

________________ (a) For respect of the rights or reputations of others; or

________________ (b) For the protection of national security or of public order (ordre public), or of public health or morals.

[...]

Extracted from: <www.ohchr.org/EN/ProfessionalInterest/Pages/CRC.aspx>. Accessed on: Jun. 27, 2016.

3. Write the correct question for the following answers.

a. ____?

Yes, I have already read the Universal Declaration of Human Rights.

b. ____?

The Universal Declaration of Human Rights was created in 1948.

4. Answer the following questions.

a. Do you know the *Estatuto da Criança e do Adolescente*? Have you ever read it?

____

b. *Estatuto da Criança e do Adolescente* was created in 1990. Do you think children and adolescents are safe and have their rights guaranteed in your community, neighborhood and city? Why?

____

Another look

TEXT 1

1. Take a look at the following text. What do you think it is?

a. ☐ news article b. ☐ biography c. ☐ fact file d. ☐ infographic

2. Read the text and check if your answer in activity 1 is correct. There is another genre that is part of the text. What is it?

____

BIS

Kids behind bars in Nauru: letters from children in immigration detention

Almost 200 children are being held in immigration detention on Nauru; some without their parents. These letters […], submitted by children to the human rights commission's inquiry into their detention, tell the story of young people missing their family, worrying about the future and seeking their freedom

Submission 147

I am an immigrant. If I was not an immigrant, why would I leave my country? I left my country because there was a war and I wanted freedom. I left my country. I came to have a better future, not to sit in a prison. If I remain in this prison, I will not have a good future. I came to become a good man in the future to help poor people. I am now 17 years old and I still cannot distinguish good from bad. I have no education and am illiterate. I am tired of life. I cannot wait much longer. What will happen to us? What are we guilty of? What have we done to be imprisoned? I do not have a good life. All the immigrants in the Australian camps do not have good lives. I am alone here on Nauru. Neither my father nor my mother is with me. It is very difficult for me to live in this prison.

In my country, there is war, murder and blood. I am Hazara and a Shiite Muslim. In my country, anyone who is a Hazara or a Shiite Muslim is killed and murdered.

POLITICAL MAP OF OCEANIA

PABLOFDEZR/SHUTTERSTOCK

If I had stayed in my country, I would have been murdered by now, because I am Hazara and a Shiite Muslim. When I arrived on Christmas Island, I did not know where I was. I remained on Christmas Island for 6 months and then I was sent to Nauru. I have been living on Nauru for 4 months, in the camp. I cannot study in this prison. I am worried about my future. What will my future be and what will happen?

Whoever reads this letter, I ask that they please help us.

I am from Afghanistan.

I have many problems in the camp. I cannot find peace. If I am released from the camp that would be good, if not, I will go crazy in this camp.

Please, please, please, read this letter carefully.

If anything can be done, please help us. Goodbye

Dear God, Please Help!

25/5/2014

Adapted from: <www.theguardian.com/world/2014/aug/15/kids-behind-bars-in-nauru-letters-from-children-in-immigration-detention>. Accessed on: Apr. 21, 2016.

3. Match the words from the text to their definitions or synonyms.

a. detention	☐	free; unconfined
b. illiterate	☐	uneducated; unschooled
c. murder	☐	homicide
d. Muslim	☐	custody; imprisonment
e. released	☐	a follower of the religion of Islam

4. Answer the following questions about the person who wrote the letter.

a. Is the person a boy or a girl? How do you know?

____

b. How old is he?

____

c. Where is he from?

____

d. Why did he leave his country?

____

____

e. What would have probably happened to him if he stayed in Afghanistan? Why?

____

____

f. What does he want to do in the future?

____

____

5. Why did he write this letter?

____

____

1. Would you leave your country? Why?

____

____

2. What do you think that can be done to help the boy and all the other people in the camp?

____

____

TEXT 2

1. Observe the text below and choose the correct sentences about it.

a. ☐ It is possible to know who wrote the text.
   ☐ It is not possible to know who wrote the text.

b. ☐ The writer hasn't included his address.
   ☐ The writer has included his address.

c. ☐ The reader knows when the text was written.
   ☐ The reader doesn't know when the text was written.

d. ☐ There is an ending.
   ☐ There isn't an ending.

2. Scan the text. Would you say the language is formal or informal?

____

3. Read the text and complete the sentence.

We can say the text has the characteristics of a ______________ (the same as "a written, typed, or printed communication, especially one sent in an envelope by mail or messenger" extracted from: <www.oxforddictionaries.com/pt/definição/inglês-americano/letter>, acessed on Jun. 27, 2016).

BIS

THEY ARE CHILDREN

Men, women, and children are joining their voices together to stand up for the brave refugee children who fled violence and hardship in Central America, seeking a chance to grow up in the United States and live happy, healthy lives.

BIS

What would you say to these children?

Dearest child,

I know your voyage here to the United States must have been very difficult and rough, my parents have also traveled to the United States to live a better life here. You are very brave to have traveled here to America. I respect that, I know many people couldn't make the journey all the way here to America. We want you to know that you are most welcome here in America, also we want you to know that when you are feeling afraid or alone, know that many people here in the United States are thinking of you. You are very very courageous to have traveled all the way to the United States all alone. We have such bright hopes for your future here in America. You deserve a life full of happiness, health and safety. We also want to wish you luck in the future. You are the kind of people America needs, brave, strong and full of hopes and dreams. We look forward to your stay here in America and your joining us and we will be here to help as much as we can. You have earned our respect, love and admiration. God bless you and have a wonderful time here in America.

Most sincerely, Rene Salcido

Rene S.

Extracted from: <www.theyarechildren.com/en/page/3>. Accessed on: Apr. 24, 2016.

4. Read the text again and answer the questions.

a. Does the writer know the person he is writing to?

____

b. Where is the child from?

____

c. Why is Rene writing to the child?

____

5. What kind of people does the writer says America needs?

____

6. Do you agree these are important personal characteristics? Why?

____

____

7. Find the reason why the writer's parents went to the US.

____

8. What would you say to a refugee child? Write a letter to support him/her.

____

____

____

____

____

BIS

1. Do you write letters? Have you ever received a letter?

____

____

2. How do teens normally communicate with each other nowadays?

____

____

Reading the world

1. Read the information below and decide whether the sentences are **T** (true) or **F** (false).

a. ☐ More than a quarter of teenagers go online quite often nowadays.

b. ☐ Most teens go online every day.

c. ☐ The Pew Research Center surveyed adolescents from thirteen to seventeen.

d. ☐ A minority goes online less than once a week.

> 24% of teens go online "almost constantly," facilitated by the widespread availability of smartphones.
> Aided by the convenience and constant access provided by mobile devices, especially smartphones, 92% of teens report going online daily — including 24% who say they go online "almost constantly," according to a new study from Pew Research Center. More than half (56%) of teens — defined in this report as those ages 13 to 17 — go online several times a day, and 12% report once-a-day use. Just 6% of teens report going online weekly, and 2% go online less often.

Extracted from: <www.pewinternet.org/2015/04/09/teens-social-media-technology-2015/>. Accessed on: Apr. 24, 2016.

2. Take a look at the picture. Do you have anything in common with those people? What?

MONKEY BUSINESS IMAGES/SHUTTERSTOCK

3. Read paragraphs 1, 2 and 3 and complete them with the expressions from the box.

face-to-face	have used some form of social media	in the digital age	in their social and emotional lives	main social networking site

BIS

www.fogcityjournal.com/wordpress/4755/teenagers-and-social-media/

1 Think back to your teenage years. How did you normally communicate? Back in the Dark Ages when I was a teenager, I communicated with my peers ______________________, by telephone, passing the occasional note in class, and reluctantly, by writing a letter. How do today's teenagers communicate ______________________? One difference, of course, is

that today's "private" communication exchanges can often be seen by the whole world, allowing the chance to comment on the exchange, and creating a permanent record of the exchange.

2 A recent survey, *Social Media, Social Life: How Teens View Their Digital Lives*, a Summer 2012 Common Sense Media Research Study attempts "to complement existing research with a broad, quantitative snapshot of how U.S. teens experience the role of social media ______________________________." [...]

Not surprisingly, the survey found that almost all teenagers in this country have used social media.

3 Nine out of ten 13 to 17-year-olds ______________________________. Three out of four teenagers currently have a profile on a social networking site, and one in five has a current Twitter account (27 percent have never used Twitter). Facebook dominates social networking use among teens: 68 percent of all teens say Facebook is their ______________________________, compared to 6 percent for Twitter, 1 percent for GooglePlus, and 1 percent for MySpace and 25 percent do not have a social networking site.

[...]

Extracted from: <www.fogcityjournal.com/wordpress/4755/teenagers-and-social-media/>. Accessed on: Apr. 24, 2016.

4. Read paragraphs 4, 5 and 6 and discuss about the underlined sentences with a classmate. Do you agree with them? Is that true in your reality? Write your conclusions in your notebook.

www.fogcityjournal.com/wordpress/4755/teenagers-and-social-media/

4 For the vast majority of teens, social and other digital communications media are a daily part of life. Two-thirds of teens text every day, half visit social networking sites daily, and 11 percent send or receive tweets at least once every day. In fact, more than a third of teens visit their main social networking site several times a day. One in four teens is a "heavy" social media user, meaning they use at least two different types of social media each and every day.

Many more teens report social media use positively on their emotional well-being than a negative one.

5 Most teens do not think their use of social media affects their social and emotional well-being one way or the other. But there are some teens who think that using social media does affect how they feel about themselves and their social situation.

6 More than one in four teens say that using their social networking site makes them feel less shy and more outgoing; one in five says it makes them feel more confident, more popular, and more sympathetic to others; and 15 percent say it makes them feel better about themselves. By comparison, only 5 percent say social networking makes them feel less outgoing; 4 percent feel worse about themselves, less confident, and less popular after using their social networking site; and 3 percent feel shyer.

[...]

Extracted from: <www.fogcityjournal.com/wordpress/4755/teenagers-and-social-media/>. Accessed on: Apr. 24, 2016.

UNIT 8

Home is where the heart is

Review the journey

1. Read about jobs in agriculture and complete the texts with the words from the boxes.

a. Agricultural Engineer

design gasoline infrastructure machinery pollution technology

Agricultural Engineering is the area of engineering concerned with the ______________________, construction and improvement of farming equipment and ______________________.

Agricultural engineers integrate ______________________ with farming. For example, they design new and improved farming equipment that may work more efficiently, or perform new tasks. They design and build agricultural ______________________ such as dams, water reservoirs, warehouses, and other structures. They may also help engineer solutions for ______________________ control at large farms. Some agricultural engineers are developing new forms of biofuels from non-food resources like algae and agricultural waste. Such fuels could economically and sustainably replace ______________________ without jeopardizing the food supply.

[...]

Extracted from: <www.environmentalscience.org/career/agricultural-engineer>. Accessed on: Jun. 6, 2016.

b. Aquatic Ecologist

balance ecology geology lakes water

Aquatic Ecology is a sub-discipline of ______________________ – the science of the environmental ______________________ between forms of the life, the geography, the ______________________ and soil type. Aquatic Ecologists examine fresh ______________________ areas such as marsh wetlands (salt flats and fresh water flood plains), ______________________ and rivers. [...]

Extracted from: <www.environmentalscience.org/career/aquatic-ecologist>. Accessed on: Jun. 6, 2016.

c. Botanist

endangered	energy	light	medicines
microscopic	nature	oxygen	plants

____________________ are vital to all life on earth. They convert ____________________ from the sun into energy we can eat, and even use for fuel. They also release the ____________________ we breathe. Botanists study plants to try to understand how these processes work. Their research is involved in enhancing crops, developing ____________________, cleaning up contaminated sites, and even powering our cars.

It's an exciting field on the cutting edge of the clean ____________________ economy. It's also a profession for ____________________ lovers. Some botanists study how plants relate to their natural communities. The work of these plant ecologists helps conserve ____________________ species and natural areas. Regardless of the specialty, we all benefit from their work.

Simply put, botany is the study of plants. While it may sound straightforward, botany includes the study of everything from algae to giant Redwood trees, from the ____________________ level to the ecosystem level.

Extracted from: <www.environmentalscience.org/career/botanist>. Accessed on: Jun. 6, 2016.

2. Finish the sentences using the passive voice.

a. In the village people eat fresh food.

Fresh food ____________________.

b. They also enjoy lots of fruits.

Lots of fruits ____________________.

3. Read the comic strip and write **T** (true) or **F** (false).

a. ☐ There is a sentence in the active voice on the board.

b. ☐ There are two sentences in the active voice on the board.

c. ☐ There is a sentence in the passive voice on the board.

"You're just messing with me, aren't you."

2015 MARK ANDERSON / DIST. BY UNIVERSAL UCLICK

4. Classify the sentences from the comic strip in passive or active voice.

a. "The sentence was written in the active voice by the boy."

____

b. "The boy wrote in the passive voice."

____

Another look

TEXT 1

1. Some people prefer living in the countryside. Others prefer living in the city. In your opinion, which arguments are in favor of village life (V) and which are in favor of city life (C)?

a. [ ] life is relatively cheap

b. [ ] people are safer and road accidents are minimised

c. [ ] hosts more diverse ways of leading a life

d. [ ] the labour market is bigger, wider and deeper

2. Read the title of the text. Do you prefer village life or city life? Read the text and check if your opinion is still the same.

___

Village life is better than city life

PRO

Living in town is not easy because life has become more expensive. You can't live in town without money, but in village you can survive because life is relatively cheap. Meanwhile criminal activities are more likely to happen in town than in the village.

In the village people eat fresh food, which they grow themselves. People in the village can also slaughter animals and get meat. They also enjoy lots of fruits. Hunger is forgotten in the village. Because of fewer vehicles in the village, people are safer and road accidents are minimised. The village also has clean air and the environment is very beautiful.

Rural life is simple. Families stay close together and care more for each other. Also, natural resources such as rivers, hills, mountains are plenty in the village. People who are living in rural areas are very important to our economy because they are the producers of food.

CON

Thank you for your arguments. To me, the arguments for living in a city clearly beat the arguments for living in the countryside.

The most important thing in life for humans is generally to love and to be loved. The risk of not finding someone to share your life with is one of the biggest fears in human life. The city offers a wide range of people, and thus a greater chance to find the perfect match. The city also hosts more diverse ways of leading a life. It is full of subcultures and niched people. To summarize the odds of finding that special someone, and to discover just what kind of life one wants to have are far greater in the city.

Another important aspect of human life is career. You want to find something meaningful, inspiring and fun to do for a living. Just stepping foot outside your apartment footstep in a big city offers great career paths. The labour market is bigger, wider and deeper. The chances of finding the job you dream about is incredibly bigger in a city compared to the country.

In a city you find most things you need close to your house. You won't need a polluting car to get what you need, just take a quick walk.

People like to do different stuff to be entertained. The supply of entertainment in a city can't be compared to that in the country. [...]

Extracted from: <www.debate.org/debates/Village-life-is-better-than-city-life/1/>. Accessed on: Apr. 25, 2016.

3. Answer the questions based on the text.

a. Where can people grow and eat fresh fruit?

____

b. Where do people usually care more for each other?

____

c. Where do people have greater chances to find the perfect match?

____

d. Where can people find the things they need close to their house?

____

4. Do you agree with the opinions in activity 3? Justify your answers with examples about where you live.

a. ______________________________

____

____

b. ______________________________

____

____

c. ______________________________

____

____

d. ______________________________

____

____

5. What do you understand by the affirmation "rural life is simple"? Do you agree with it?

____

____

____

1. According to everything you read and discussed in this Unit, do you think there is one place that is better to live than the other, or is it just a personal opinion? Justify your answer.

____

____

2. If you could choose any place on earth to live, where would it be and why?

____

____

TEXT 2

1. The text *Village life is better than city life*, on page 58, mentions a few pros and cons of living in urban and rural areas. The text presents

a. ☐ arguments
b. ☐ different positions
c. ☐ controversies
d. ☐ physical attacks
e. ☐ an audience
f. ☐ points of view

2. The text below also presents a set of different opinions. Would you say the text looks like a speech or a debate? Read it and check your answer.

____

3. Why do you think so many people debate about which lifestyle is better?

____

____

____

Is urban living better than rural living?

BIS

51% Say Yes	49% Say No
For most people, yes. It is hard to say whether a particular style of living is better for any single person. But the historic evidence is clear that for the growth and expansion of civilization, urban centers are where ideas are exchanged, where most education and research happens, and where artistic and creative pursuits thrive the most. It is also where more people, proportionally, rise out of poverty compared to rural areas, which is exactly why Chinese gravitate toward their cities and away from the countryside. One has more opportunity. From an environment standpoint, cities are also denser and surprisingly better suited to deal with global warming.	**Urban people are missing the life they need to be living.** REASONS: pollution, overcrowded, crimes and killings, can't trust people in the city and higher property costs in general. Also need permits in urban areas just about all the time, traffic is terrible which means horrible transportation other than the wired people on metro. TRASH IS EVERYWHERE. UNDISCIPLINED FOOLISH PEOPLE NOT ALL BUT MANY IN THE CITY. Lastly you can do almost whatever you want as long as you keep the peace and it is legal. One more thing to add is food comes from rural areas and into food markets, wildlife is cleansing to the mind, teaches you how to respect creation and life itself as well as other people [...]
2 4	0 0

Extracted from: <www.debate.org/opinions/is-urban-living-better-than-rural-living>. Accessed on: Apr. 25, 2016.

4. Read and rewrite the sentences. Correct the wrong information.

a. The person who prefers urban life believes that rural areas are where ideas are exchanged. This person also believes that urban areas are places where, proportionally, less people rise out of poverty.

____

____

____

b. The person who prefers country life believes that cities are overcrowded and clean. This person also believes that wildlife harms the mind.

____

____

____

5. What do the percentages of negative and positive answers to the debate tell you? Do people have a consensus about living in the country or in the city?

____

____

____

____

6. Read the following sentence again.

> "[...] historic evidence is clear that for the growth and expansion of civilization, urban centers are where ideas are exchanged, where most education and research happens, and where artistic and creative pursuits thrive the most. [...]"

Do you agree with it? Can you mention any historical event to prove this affirmation to be true?

____

____

____

1. Have you ever participated in a debate? How did you feel? Do you think your arguments were convincing? What could you improve in your debating skills?

____

____

2. Do you follow any kind of debates? For example, what do you think of political debates? Are they necessary?

____

____

Reading the world

1. No matter where people live, in New Zealand or in Paraguay, in the city or in a village, they may feel bored. Read the comic strips and say what both have in common.

2. Match questions and answers.

Questions		Answers
a. What is Jon, Garfield's owner, planning to do?	☐	To go to a summer camp.
b. Who says he needs a change of settings?	☐	He is planning to visit his parents.
c. How does Garfield usually feel?	☐	No, they'd rather stay.
d. What does the kids' mom suggest them to do?	☐	Garfield does.
e. Who will find peace and quiet while the children are in summer camp?	☐	Mom will.
f. Do the children feel like traveling?	☐	He usually feels bored.

3. Do you think the countryside mentioned in the comic strips is the same thing as life in the countryside people discuss in the debates you read? Why?

____

____

____

____

____

4. What do you prefer: urban or rural living? Write three advantages and three disadvantages (different from the ones described in the previous texts) of living in this place.

Advantages

a. ______________________________

____

____

b. ______________________________

____

____

c. ______________________________

____

____

Disadvantages

d. ______________________________

____

____

e. ______________________________

____

____

f. ______________________________

____

____

5. Imagine you are on vacation. Where would you like to travel to: the countryside or the city? Why?

____

____

____

____

____

____

Connecting ideas

UNIT 1

- **www.rogerebert.com/reviews/fried-green-tomatoes-1992**
  Fried Green Tomatoes – movie review
- **www.youtube.com/watch?v=mZUea1yIWKQ**
  Wrinkles – movie trailer
- **www.youtube.com/watch?v=dj_3yY7VA6o**
  O ciclo da vida – movie trailer
- **www.planalto.gov.br/ccivil_03/leis/2003/L10.741.htm**
  Estatuto do Idoso

UNIT 2

- **www.expatsblog.com/contests/431/my-experience-with-culture-shock-in-america-american-raised-abroad**
  My experience with culture shock in America as an American raised abroad, by Bonnie Rose
- **http://www.nydailynews.com/life-style/dangers-posting-photos-online-article-1.1432134**
  The dangers of posting photos online

UNIT 3

- **www.youtube.com/watch?v=bpAS5f4TjNw**
  Who Are Australia's Aboriginal People?
- **www.youtube.com/watch?v=G8czHlPYXew**
  Aboriginal People Respond to "Australia Day"
- **www.youtube.com/watch?v=fP4b1iHnsak**
  Tourist Attractions in Kristiansand, Norway
- **www.youtube.com/watch?v=50lL7D2Dec8**
  Jamaican Rice and Peas Recipe

UNIT 4

- **http://taylorswift.com/**
  Taylor Swift's official website
- **www.jasonisbell.com/**
  Jason Isbell's official website
- **www.bonjovi.com/**
  Bon Jovi's official website

UNIT 5

- **www.heforshe.org/en**
  HeForShe organization official website
- **www.youtube.com/watch?v=Y07Znu8rGP0**
  Mona Lisa's Smile – movie trailer
- **www.youtube.com/watch?v=DZ509hHkHO8**
  Made in Dagenham – movie trailer
- **www.biography.com/people/mark-twain-9512564**
  Mark Twain's biography
- **www.youtube.com/watch?v=UVTMkINRChk**
  The Help – movie trailer

UNIT 6

- **www.youtube.com/watch?v=oGab38pKscw**
  The High Price of Materialism
- **www.youtube.com/watch?v=9GorqroigqM**
  Story of Stuff
- **http://www.metrolyrics.com/royals-lyrics-lorde.html**
  "Royals", by Lorde

UNIT 7

- **www.ohchr.org/EN/ProfessionalInterest/Pages/CRC.aspx**
  Convention on the Rights of the Child
- **ww.youtube.com/watch?v=Cnc4LaevRBw**
  Internet Safety Tips for Teens
- **www.youtube.com/watch?v=yrln8nyVBLU**
  Safe Web Surfing: Top Tips for Kids and Teens Online
- **www.pewinternet.org/2015/04/09/teens-social-media-technology-2015/**
  Teens, Social Media & Technology Overview 2015

UNIT 8

- **www.canalrural.com.br/noticias/carreiras/agricultura-lidera-geracao-postos-trabalho-62252**
  Article about the growth of jobs in agriculture in Brazil
- **www.cnbc.com/2015/05/20/agriculture-fertile-ground-for-job-seekers.html**
  Agriculture: Job growth to boom over next five years
- **http://livingstandards1920s.weebly.com/city-life.html**
  How did living standards change in the 1920's?